THE LITTLE BOOK
OF COLOURING

TROPICAL
PARADISE

PEACE IN
YOUR POCKET

Other books in
THE LITTLE BOOK OF COLOURING
series:

Animal Kingdom
In Bloom
Patterns

Published in the UK in 2015 by

Quercus Publishing Ltd
Carmelite House
50 Victoria Embankment
London EC4Y 0DZ

An Hachette UK company

A CIP catalogue record for this book is available
from the British Library

ISBN 978 1 78429 642 1

10 9 8 7 6 5 4 3 2 1

Designed and typeset by Carrdesignstudio.com
Printed and bound in the UK by Clays Ltd, St Ives plc

THE LITTLE BOOK
OF COLOURING

TROPICAL PARADISE

PEACE IN
YOUR POCKET

ILLUSTRATED BY
AMBER ANDERSON

Quercus

If things in your life are tasting bitter,

eat something else.

I'm not afraid of storms, for I'm
learning to sail my ship.

Louisa May Alcott

A smile cures more than any medicine.

Be bold with your goals; if you remain in familiar territory you will never experience the thrill of the unknown.

The more you believe in yourself, the more others will put their belief in you, too.

I love tranquil solitude

And such society

As is quiet, wise and good.

Percy Bysshe Shelley

If you want to fly, just spread your wings.

If you feel scared about what's ahead,
look to others who got there before you.

Anyone can hold the helm

when the sea is calm.

Publilius Syrus

As you go the way of life you will see a great
chasm. Jump. It is not as wide as you think.

Native American proverb

A peace above all earthly dignities,

a still and quiet conscience.

William Shakespeare

Patience is bitter, but its fruit is sweet.

Jean-Jacques Rousseau

If you open your eyes and heart to the love
around you, it can only lift your spirits.

What does not kill me makes me stronger.

Johann Wolfgang von Goethe

To see a world in a grain of sand

And a heaven in a wild flower,

Hold infinity in the palm of your hand

And eternity in an hour.

William Blake

Nothing can bring you peace but yourself.

Ralph Waldo Emerson

The sky is not the limit:

there's a whole universe beyond it!

In nature things move violently to their place,

and calmly in their place.

Francis Bacon

We must walk consciously only part way
toward our goal and then leap in the dark
to our success.

Henry David Thoreau

A heart that loves is always young.

Greek proverb

You are not alone on your journey through life – walk with others and find the joy and support in shared experiences.

Believe that you are moving in the
right direction. Follow your feet and trust
that you are choosing the best path.

The people who love you most will give
you the freedom to be what you want.
Show others that same love.

To sit in the shade on a fine day,
and look upon verdure is the most
perfect refreshment.

Jane Austen

When once you have tasted flight,

you will forever walk the earth with your eyes

turned skyward, for there you have been,

and there you long to return.

Leonardo da Vinci

Say to yourself, 'The world is a wonderful place and I am lucky to be a part of it!'

You are who you are. Love yourself, cherish your qualities and marvel at your uniqueness. The more you love and respect yourself, the more others will love and respect you.

Fairy tales are more than true. Not because they tell us that dragons exist, but because they tell us that dragons can be defeated.

G. K. Chesterton

Help others to help you. Allow them to show you their love and support. You need not be alone in your troubles.

With time and patience the mulberry leaf

becomes silk.

Chinese proverb

Whatever you do, give it your all.
Throw yourself in with confidence,
and throw doubts and fears aside.

Remember to preserve a
calm soul amid difficulties.

Horace

Sitting quietly, doing nothing, spring comes,

and the grass grows by itself.

Zen saying

Give your best every day,
for we have the power to make
the world as good as we want.

Where there are friends there is wealth.

Titus Maccius Plautus

We must always change, renew, rejuvenate ourselves; otherwise, we harden.

Johann Wolfgang von Goethe

Live every day with love, not fear.

Dare to live the life you dream of and

watch your dreams come true.

Have faith that you will experience joy and contentment today and every day.

Treat others with kindness and trust that
your kindnesses will be repaid.

Always do what you are afraid to do.

Ralph Waldo Emerson

If the world were good for nothing else,

it is a fine subject for speculation.

William Hazlitt

Peace comes from within.

Do not seek it without.

Buddha

The good and the wise lead quiet lives.

Euripides

We are all students and we are all teachers.
If we open our minds, and share our
experience and knowledge generously
with others, our lives will be richer for it.

Why rush forward to the future when there is so much to appreciate today? Stop, look around you and decide that today you will see only those things that are positive in your life. The bad can wait for another day.